Reading Comprehension

Book 4

Jo Browning Wroe
David Lambert

Reading Comprehension Book 4
MT00750
ISBN-13: 978 1 85503 384 9
ISBN-10: 1 85503 384 4
© Jo Browning Wroe and David Lambert
Cover illustrations © Sally Launder, David Pattison and Caroline Sharpe
Illustrations © Lizzie Finlay, Sally Launder, David Pattison and Caroline Sharpe
All rights reserved
First published 2003
Reprinted 2004, 2005 (twice), 2006

Printed in the UK for LDA
Abbeygate House, East Road,
Cambridge, CB1 1DB, UK

Contents

Teacher's notes

Each book in the LDA Reading Comprehension series provides up to 33 stimulating photocopiable comprehension activities for the children you teach. In line with the National Literacy Strategy, the books present a wide variety of text types, including newspaper articles, poetry, dialogue, prose, instructions, charts and tables, letters, guidebook information and journal entries.

The activities are graded so that you will find a general trend of increasing conceptual complexity or discoursal organisation within the texts as you move through each section.

The four skill areas

To develop and hone your pupils' skills in four crucial areas of reading comprehension, the activities are grouped under the following headings:

Getting the main idea

In these activities, the pupils' overall grasp of the text is tested. To answer the questions, they are required to use their overall understanding of the text's main theme, argument or development.

Making inferences

The questions in this section encourage the pupils to make connections between the discrete elements embedded in the text. Pupils must choose, from a range of possibilities, the answer that is most *likely* to be true.

Noting details

Here, pupils are invited to scan the text for information and to retrieve discrete facts, for example an opening time, a date, or a figure. Occasionally, a more systematic reading is required to grasp the relationship between facts embedded in the text.

Using context clues

The questions in these activities encourage pupils to be sleuths, searching the textual environment for *clues* in order to select the most appropriate words or phrases to fill the blanks and complete the passage.

The questions

For each activity there are five questions that relate directly to the text. In most cases these are multiple choice and pupils simply have to circle the letters to indicate their answers. For the Noting details activities, pupils are required to write in their own answers.

At the end of each activity, there is a sixth, open-ended extension question. This is designed to encourage further reading, research, reflection or creativity on the same topic or a related one. These questions aim to personalise the text, making the issues raised within it relevant to the reader. There are three types of extension question:

Ask yourself

These questions tend to have an ethical slant and seek to develop pupils' critical thinking skills. For example, after an article about the origin of jeans:

Do you think we have become obsessed with fashion? Should advertisements and magazine articles decide what we wear?

Find out for yourself

These questions put the pupils in charge of their learning, inviting them to find out more about a subject. This might be done in a number of different ways, for example by using books, searching on the Web or asking people questions. It is usually left to the pupil to identify their own sources of reference, as each of these questions is very much a point of departure, not an end in itself. For example, following a text about

Leonardo da Vinci:

Find out where the Mona Lisa *is hung and why it is thought to be such a great painting.*

Express yourself

These questions encourage pupils to respond imaginatively and creatively to the texts they have read. They might be asked to write prose or poetry or to draw, design or make something. For example:

Imagine you are the archaeologist who discovered the trepanned skull. Write your journal entry for that day. Include the thoughts that were going through your mind as you uncovered and then examined the skull.

How do I use the book?

These Reading Comprehension books are intended to be a flexible teaching resource to use in the way that best enhances the learning going on in your classroom. The activities will fit well into the small group section of the literacy hour, but this is by no means the only appropriate context for the material. At the beginning of a school year, for example, they could be used as a tool to assess your pupils' level of comprehension and to find if there are particular areas of weakness which can then be addressed.

The texts should take no longer than 10 minutes to read and the questions no more than another 10 minutes to complete, although this will vary greatly from pupil to pupil.

In some circumstances, it may be beneficial for pupils to tackle the activities in pairs. In this way, less able pupils who lack confidence can provide each other with support as they read and then answer the questions.

There might also be occasions when it is helpful for a pupil to have access to the answers, in order to check their own work.

Answers

An answer key is provided at the back of the book on page 64.

The Fighting Spiders of Japan

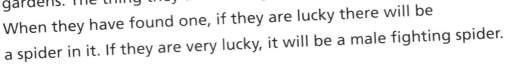

In Japan there is a traditional game played by children and some adults that has been passed down from generation to generation. Before the game can be played, there is something the players have to find. They have to get up early and search among the bushes in their gardens. The thing they are looking for is a web. When they have found one, if they are lucky there will be a spider in it. If they are very lucky, it will be a male fighting spider.

Spider contests are as common in Japan as games of marbles are in Britain. The spider is kept in a little box, then brought out and put on a table opposite another spider. When the two spiders are together, they become angry and fight until one gives up or runs away.

Some adults keep fighting spiders. They raise them specially for an annual contest in which the champion arachnid wins a prize.

Spider fighting seems an odd sport to us, but it has been a pastime in Japan for many years. Japanese children probably think it is played all over the world.

The Fighting Spiders of Japan

Read the text carefully and circle the best ending for each sentence.

1. Spider fighting has been played in Japan
   a) for a very long time.
   b) for two generations.
   c) since the beginning of the twentieth century.

2. If you want to play the game, you need to find
   a) lots of webs.
   b) a male spider.
   c) lots of luck.

3. The spider is put on a table to fight
   a) a female fighting spider.
   b) another male fighting spider.
   c) two other fighting spiders.

4. Spider fighting is played by
   a) children only.
   b) adults only.
   c) children and adults.

5. Japanese children probably view spider fighting as
   a) normal.
   b) unusual.
   c) old fashioned.

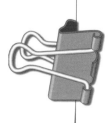

Ask yourself

Do you agree with spider fighting? Think about the possible arguments on both sides, then write one paragraph defending the game and one condemning it.

Scribble

Do you remember when you were very young, wishing that you could read and write like your parents, or your older brother or sister? Did you ever send relatives or friends thank-you letters, which had lots of swirls and scribbles that you called words?

Years ago, no one took much notice of young children's scribble. People thought it was just 'playing' at writing. Nowadays, educational experts say that encouraging very young children to scribble – even before they know their alphabet – is very important. The scribbling stage is now considered to be a vital step in the development of real writing. The chaotic lines and shapes on a page may not look like words that can be read, but experts suggest they should still be viewed as writing. Teachers are taught to invite children to 'read' their writing aloud, even if it is illegible.

You might think that all this is just a big game of pretend. But educationists believe that because scribble is an important step on the path to fluent writing, it should be taken seriously. There is now considerable evidence to demonstrate that children who are encouraged in their attempts at writing before they are 5 years old grow up to be better readers.

Scribble

Read the text carefully and circle the best ending for each sentence.

1. This passage is about how
   a) we should all scribble more.
   b) children learn to write.
   c) adults do not understand children.

2. Children's play is now thought to be
   a) an important part of the learning process.
   b) more important than school work.
   c) a waste of time.

3. Children can benefit from scribbling
   a) only after they have learned the alphabet.
   b) before they have learned the alphabet.
   c) instead of learning the alphabet.

4. Scribbling should be taken seriously because
   a) children's feelings are easily hurt.
   b) it is very creative.
   c) it is a stage in learning to write.

5. Evidence shows that learning to read and learning to write
   a) is a game of pretend.
   b) is best done in school.
   c) are closely linked.

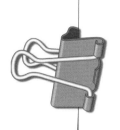

Ask yourself

Do you remember pretending to write before you really could? What do you remember most clearly from your first year at school?

Out and About

Days out

in country houses

Our country is full of places that are historical treasures – many not as well known as they deserve to be. Starting this issue, *Out and About* will be featuring a different National Trust property each week. We hope every reader will be inspired to visit some of the history on their doorstep. And if you enter our competition by emailing us your details, you could win free entry to the house featured that week!

Ickworth House

If you're looking for a country house with a difference, then look no further than Ickworth. Built by the eccentric Fourth Earl of Bristol in the eighteenth century, the main body of the house is circular with corridors curving off to the sides. It was so far from the kitchens to the dining room that servants cycled along the basement corridors!

The gardens are no less magnificent, with massive stones brought from the Giant's Causeway, a collection of tree stumps, a cycle route and a very challenging children's play area. Also for the children, there is a variety of trails around the park, an area for ball games and deer to spot.

When?	House: Fri–Tues, 1–5 p.m. Park and gardens: daily 10 a.m.–5 p.m.
How much?	House and park: adults £6.10, children £2.75. Park: £2.80/80p
Events	Easter Bunny Day: Fri 18th 11 a.m.–4 p.m., £2 per child
	Easter Trail: Sun 20th and Mon 21st, 11 a.m.–4 p.m., £2 per child

Out and About

Read the text carefully and circle the best ending for each sentence.

1 *Out and About* magazine suggests that
   a) people know about most of the country's historical buildings.
   b) people should get out more often.
   c) people do not appreciate the country's historical buildings.

2 Ickworth House would be a good place to visit
   a) if you like traditional houses.
   b) if you enjoy unusual architecture.
   c) if you like walking a long way.

3 The Fourth Earl of Bristol, who built Ickworth House,
   a) had an unusual approach to things.
   b) liked to copy what other people had done.
   c) loved cycling indoors.

4 A day out at Ickworth
   a) would be boring for children.
   b) would have things to interest adults and children.
   c) would not be suitable for adults.

5 If you wanted to visit Ickworth, you could go
   a) any weekday, but not at a weekend.
   b) any day except Wednesday and Thursday.
   c) only at a weekend.

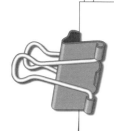

Express yourself

Design your own stately home. You might like to find out more about some others before you start.

Life Support

You have probably looked at a piece of animal bone. It might be hard to imagine that our bodies are held together by similar pieces of this hard material. What you may not realise is that the bones in our bodies are living tissue – just like our heart, lungs and other organs.

Together, our bones make up our skeleton, which provides the structure for our bodies. It supports the muscles and organs and gives the body its shape. Bones become thicker and stronger as we develop. If our bones didn't grow, we couldn't grow!

Like all the other parts of our body, bones need nourishment to stay healthy and to function properly. All bones are supplied with blood vessels that constantly bring food and oxygen. Inside the bone, special cells called osteoclasts and osteoblasts continually work to rebuild bone tissue, repairing the damage from the wear and tear of daily living.

The bones also contain connective tissue called marrow. Yellow bone marrow contains fat, and red bone marrow makes red and white blood cells and blood platelets. These blood cells are very important and you quickly become very sick if your body fails to produce them.

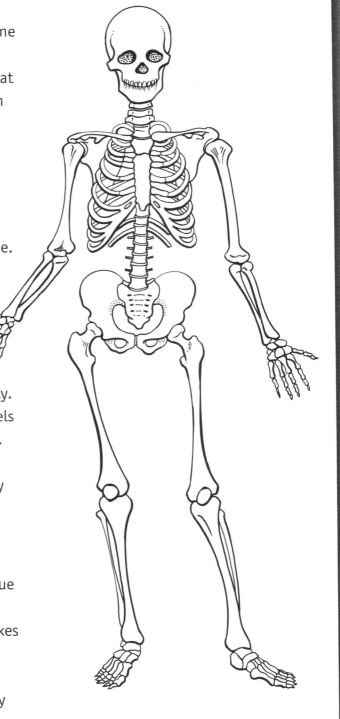

Life Support

Read the text carefully and circle the best ending for each sentence.

1. The main point this writer wants to put across is that bones are
   - a) strong and hard.
   - b) living organs.
   - c) the same in animals and people.

2. Without bones, our bodies would have no
   - a) structure.
   - b) organs.
   - c) nourishment.

3. Bones need nourishment, which they get from
   - a) special cells.
   - b) oxygen.
   - c) blood.

4. The cells of bones need to be replaced because
   - a) they get old quickly.
   - b) of daily wear and tear.
   - c) of osteoblasts and osteoclasts.

5. Red bone marrow is essential for
   - a) healthy blood.
   - b) making fat for the body.
   - c) healthy bones.

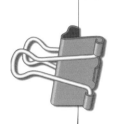

Find out for yourself

Find out the names of the different bones in your body.
Draw a skeleton and label the bones.

Windy Willows

A letter from Anne Shirley, BA, Principal of Summerside High School, to Gilbert Blythe, medical student at Redmond College, Kingsport

Windy Willows
Spook's Lane
S'side
P. E. I.
Monday, Sept. 12

DEAREST,

Isn't that an address! Did you ever hear anything so delicious? Windy Willows is the name of my new home and I love it. I also love Spook's Lane, which has no legal existence. It should be Trent Street, but it is never called Trent Street except on the rare occasion when it is mentioned in the *Weekly Courier* – and then people look at each other and say, 'Where on earth is that?' Spook's Lane it is – although for what reason I cannot tell you. I have already asked Rebecca Dew about it, but all she can say is that it has always been Spook's Lane, and there was some old yarn years ago of its being haunted. But *she* has never seen anything worse looking than herself in it.

However, I mustn't get ahead of my story. You don't know Rebecca Dew yet. But you will – oh, yes, you will! I foresee that Rebecca Dew will figure largely in my future correspondence.

Extract from *Anne of Windy Willows*
by L. M. Montgomery

Windy Willows

Read the text carefully and circle the best ending for each sentence.

1. Gilbert Blythe is probably
   a) Anne's father.
   b) Anne's brother.
   c) Anne's boyfriend.

2. Anne is
   a) homesick.
   b) enthusiastic about her new home.
   c) scared of ghosts.

3. The *Weekly Courier* must be
   a) the local newspaper.
   b) the postal service.
   c) an Indian restaurant.

4. Rebecca Dew
   a) thinks Spook's Lane is haunted.
   b) thinks she is a ghost.
   c) has heard stories about Spook's Lane being haunted.

5. Anne thinks that Rebecca is going to
   a) scare her.
   b) become good friends with Gilbert.
   c) become a good friend of hers.

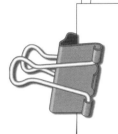

Express yourself

Write a description of Spook's Lane and make up a story about how it got its name. It could be scary, but it could also be funny.

Professor Stephen Hawking

Professor Stephen Hawking is Professor of Mathematics and Physics at the University of Cambridge, England.

You may have heard about his mind-boggling ideas about space and time. If you have seen him on television, you will probably remember him. He sits in a wheelchair and has movement only in one finger. He has no voice and has to speak in an American accent using a computer-driven speech synthesiser. He has a condition called motor neurone disease, which has been gradually wasting his muscles away since he was 21. Because of his disability, all his incredible mathematical calculations are done in his head. He has been called the greatest genius since Einstein.

Professor Hawking is best known for his theories about the universe, which he says is only a tiny part of a 'super universe'. This super universe is infinite; in other words it goes on forever. It has also existed forever. His pioneering work in this field has won him prizes from around the world.

Ideas about black holes are another well-known part of Professor Hawking's work. A black hole is an area out in space where the gravity pull is so great that everything nearby gets sucked into it. Time in a black hole is believed to stand still. So if an astronaut were to fall into one, he would not age. Physicists like Professor Hawking believe that in a black hole, time may even go backwards. So the unfortunate astronaut might even get younger!

Professor Stephen Hawking

Read the text carefully and circle the best ending for each sentence.

1 Professor Hawking speaks with an American accent because
   a) he is American.
   b) his speech synthesiser produces an American voice.
   c) he has motor neurone disease.

2 An infinite universe is one that
   a) does not have an end.
   b) is very big.
   c) we cannot measure.

3 Professor Hawking has won prizes
   a) for doing calculations in his head.
   b) because he has motor neurone disease.
   c) for his theories about space and time.

4 In black holes
   a) there is no gravity.
   b) astronauts get younger.
   c) the normal laws of time and space are changed.

5 What Professor Hawking says about black holes
   a) must be a joke.
   b) is a theory.
   c) has been proved.

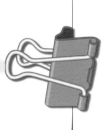

Ask yourself

Do you think there might be other planets with life somewhere in the universe, or is our planet the only one?

Andes Adventure

A 9-night tour visiting Lima, Machu Picchu and the Sacred Valley of the Incas

From £999

Lake Titicaca option from £129 extra

A unique holiday in a land steeped in history

Gaze in awe at the soaring peaks of the Andes – said by many to be the world's most magnificent and imposing mountain range. Listen to the haunting sounds of the traditional Pan pipes; take a spectacular train ride through the Andes to Machu Picchu, 'The Lost City of the Incas'; admire the brilliantly coloured artefacts produced by the weavers and potters; and enjoy the beauty and symmetry of the Spanish colonial architecture.

Our itinerary is designed so that you can take in the full range of sights, beginning with a stay in Lima. Your first night in the high Andes is spent in the pretty mountain village of Yukay, set in the fertile Sacred Valley of the Incas, some 600 metres lower than Cusco. This allows you to acclimatise to the altitude as well as seeing the 'true' Andes and their fascinating way of life.

Andes Adventure

Read the text carefully and circle the best ending for each sentence.

1. People might take this tour if they wanted a holiday with
   a) mountaineering.
   b) spectacular scenery and historical interest.
   c) music and entertainment.

2. The Andes mountain range
   a) is definitely the most magnificent in the world.
   b) is similar to most other mountain ranges round the world.
   c) is among the most impressive in the world.

3. A trip to the Andes gives you the chance to see
   a) a very different way of life from that in Britain.
   b) customs and traditions similar to those in Britain.
   c) some spectacular trains.

4. The mountain village of Yukay
   a) takes some getting used to.
   b) will help you get used to the high altitude.
   c) is at a higher altitude than any other mountain village.

5. In Yukay you can
   a) be a tourist.
   b) see Cusco.
   c) see how people really live in the Andes.

Express yourself

Is there somewhere in the world you would love to visit?
Write about it and explain why it appeals to you.

To Autumn

Season of mists and mellow fruitfulness,

Close bosom-friend of the maturing sun;

Conspiring with him how to load and bless

With fruit the vines that round the thatch-eves run;

To bend with apples the moss'd cottage-trees,

And fill all fruit with ripeness to the core;

To swell the gourd, and plump the hazel shells

With a sweet kernel; to set budding more,

And still more, later flowers for the bees,

Until they think warm days will never cease,

For Summer has o'er-brimmed their clammy cells.

Verse one of 'To Autumn' by John Keats

To Autumn

Read the text carefully and circle the best ending for each sentence.

1 The poet thinks that autumn is
   a) a miserable time of year.
   b) a wonderful time of year.
   c) time to collect all the fruit off the trees.

2 During the autumn, the poet thinks of the sun as
   a) fresh and young.
   b) tired.
   c) fully grown.

3 The poet describes autumn and the sun as
   a) friends.
   b) enemies.
   c) husband and wife.

4 Keats writes about how autumn fruit is
   a) ripe and mouldy.
   b) too heavy for the trees.
   c) ripe and plentiful.

5 Keats describes autumn days as often
   a) chilly.
   b) as warm as the summer.
   c) clammy.

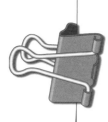

Find out for yourself

Read the rest of this poem by John Keats.

Trepanning

Surprising as it may seem, archaeologists have uncovered evidence to suggest that delicate surgical procedures were practised successfully over 5,000 years ago.

When an ancient skull was discovered in France, it was found to have two holes where small pieces of bone had been removed. One hole was nearly 6 cm across and the other nearly 8 cm. Archaeologists were fascinated. It was significant that there was no indication that the person had died a violent death. Furthermore, because the skull had started to grow back, the patient must have survived the operation.

It is thought that the holes were caused by a procedure called trepanation. The oldest surgical procedure known to us, it involves removing a small piece of bone from the skull by cutting or drilling. We do not know for sure why this was done. However, the operation is still practised in Africa today to cure various illnesses, and experts imagine that ancient people did it for similar reasons. It is believed they used it to treat pressure on the brain, recurrent headaches, epilepsy and mental illness.

It is thought that the holes in the skull found in France were carefully scraped and cut into the bone using sharpened flint. From that skull, experts deduce that the procedure must date earlier than 3,000 BC. Such a delicate operation must have been practised over many years for it not to kill the patient.

Trepanning

Read the text carefully and circle the best ending for each sentence.

① We tend to think that surgery is
   a) an ancient practice.
   b) a modern practice.
   c) a dangerous practice.

② To find a 5,000-year-old skull with evidence of surgery was
   a) amazing.
   b) common.
   c) devastating.

③ If there was evidence that the operation had killed the patient,
   a) the discovery would not have been so surprising.
   b) the discovery would have been even more surprising.
   c) the discovery would have changed the course of history.

④ Experts can work out likely reasons for the trepanation by
   a) reading old surgical manuals.
   b) finding out why it is practised in Africa today.
   c) studying the 5,000-year-old skull.

⑤ The surgical procedure of trepanning must have been
   a) fairly easy to do.
   b) extremely rare.
   c) very difficult to do.

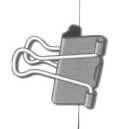

Express yourself

Imagine you are the archaeologist who discovered the trepanned skull. Write your journal entry for that day. Try to include the thoughts that were going through your mind as you uncovered and then examined the skull.

The Holmsworth Herald   2 June 2003

Letters to the Editor

I read your article about professional footballers with dismay. I think it is a disgrace that footballers are given so much status in this country. They get paid astronomical amounts of money just for playing a stupid game. They are given expensive designer clothing when they are some of the few people who could actually afford to buy it. And they don't even have to work the whole year round.

Football is just a game. Instead of worshipping a bunch of men who happen to be good at kicking a ball around, we should give respect to the people who really make a difference in this world.

Colin Needly

I am writing in wholehearted support of the article in last week's *Herald* – we should indeed give credit to our professional footballers. I think they provide a vital role model for children today. They demonstrate what can be achieved through hard work and dedication. Kids today need to be inspired to try harder and be the very best that they can. It brings tears to my eyes to see a group of healthy, committed lads playing together as a team and achieving their dreams.

If it wasn't for them, thousands of kids would be sitting watching TV every day instead of going outside to practise their own footballing skills.

James Oville

Letters to the Editor

Read the text carefully and circle the best ending for each sentence.

1. Colin Needly

   a) likes football but does not respect footballers.
   b) does not like football or respect footballers.
   c) does not like football but respects footballers.

2. Colin Needly thinks that

   a) most people have to work harder than footballers.
   b) the football season is too long.
   c) footballers never have a holiday.

3. James Oville thinks that

   a) footballers love children.
   b) children should all want to be footballers.
   c) footballers set a good example for children.

4. James Oville believes in

   a) accepting your lot in life.
   b) striving to reach your full potential.
   c) crying at football matches.

5. James Oville thinks that professional footballers

   a) motivate children to do more sport.
   b) encourage children to watch lots of sport on television.
   c) never watch television.

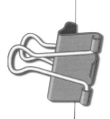

Ask yourself

What is your opinion on this subject? Write your own letter to the editor and include reasons for each of your points.

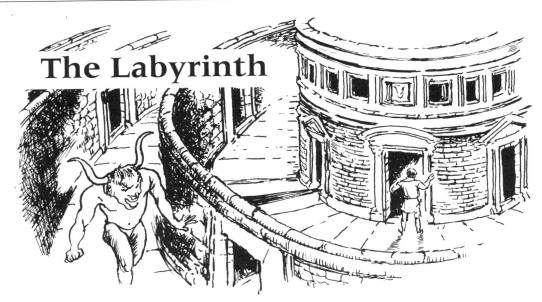

The Labyrinth

Perhaps you have played labyrinth games on a computer.
They can be pretty mind-boggling.

The word 'labyrinth' comes from an ancient Greek myth.
The Labyrinth was a huge maze, built on the order of King
Minos of Crete and designed by an inventor called Daedelus.
Once it was built, the Labyrinth was used to imprison a terrible
monster called the Minotaur, which had the body of a man and
the head of a bull.

King Minos had a terrible custom of sacrificing seven young
men and seven young women from nearby Athens every year
by sending them into the maze to be eaten by the Minotaur.
One year, a prince from Athens volunteered to go as a sacrifice.
He wanted to put a stop to the annual slaughter by killing the
Minotaur and then finding his way out.

When the prince arrived on the island of Crete, the daughter
of King Minos fell in love with him. She gave him the end of
a silken thread to take into the Labyrinth. She kept hold of the
other end so he could use it to find his way out.

Not only did the prince kill the Minotaur; he was able to rescue
the 13 other Athenians and find his way out of the maze. Thus
he ensured that no more of his people were sacrificed.

The Labyrinth

Read the text carefully and circle the best ending for each sentence.

1. Labyrinth computer games are so called because
   a) they are based on a maze, like the Labyrinth in the Greek myth.
   b) they are mind-boggling.
   c) Labyrinth is the name of the manufacturer.

2. The Labyrinth designed by Daedelus was probably
   a) made of steel.
   b) extremely complicated.
   c) very beautiful.

3. The prince of Athens
   a) knew a lot about labyrinths.
   b) was very brave.
   c) had a good sense of direction.

4. The prince was very fortunate
   a) to arrive in Crete.
   b) to find the silken thread.
   c) to be helped by the daughter of King Minos.

5. After killing the Minotaur, the prince of Athens must have been
   a) proud.
   b) angry.
   c) jealous.

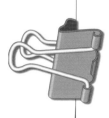

Express yourself

Imagine you are the prince of Athens. Write a description of entering the Labyrinth and coming face to face with the Minotaur. Find an imaginative way to describe how frightening the monster is.

The Round Table

The Round Table is central to the legend of King Arthur. More than an actual table, it represents a set of ideals.

The table itself was large and circular, with a place for each of King Arthur's knights.

Different writers claim different numbers of places at the table: some say as few as 24, others as many as 250. One twelfth-century writer said that the Round Table could seat as many as 1,600 people! There were several Round Tables in existence during the Middle Ages.

One of them, without its legs, hangs today in the great hall at Winchester Castle.

The ideals represented by the Round Table are those of friendship and chivalry. All the knights were bound by an oath to serve King Arthur and be loyal to him. Together, they would fight for good and against evil. Because the table was round, no one position was more important than any other; all the knights were equal.

Medieval writers compared the Round Table to the table used by Christ and his disciples at the Last Supper. Judas left the table to betray Jesus and his place was left empty. Similarly, one seat was always left empty at the Round Table. This served to highlight the connection between King Arthur and the Knights of the Round Table, and Christ and his disciples.

The Round Table

Read the text carefully and circle the best ending for each sentence.

1. The Round Table represented

   a) a large gathering of people.
   b) the qualities King Arthur and his knights thought were important.
   c) different things according to different writers.

2. The details about the Round Table vary in different stories,

   a) but it always stands for friendship and honour.
   b) and it is not always circular.
   c) but only one version can tell us the truth.

3. The table that hangs in Winchester Castle

   a) is the original Round Table.
   b) cannot be the original Round Table.
   c) may be the original Round Table.

4. The Knights of the Round Table

   a) fought against wrong.
   b) were very ambitious.
   c) envied King Arthur.

5. Medieval writers

   a) believed King Arthur was divine.
   b) thought that in some ways King Arthur was like Jesus.
   c) thought that the Round Table had been used by Jesus.

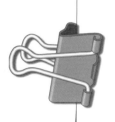

Ask yourself

Do you believe that we are all equal, like the Knights of the Round Table? Or do you think some people should be treated with more respect than others?

The Exchange Visit

Thanks and sorry - message

Draft   Save   Attach   Spelling   Receipt   Send

To: ▷ Hans   Add Cc   Add Bcc

Subject: Thanks and sorry

Copy to: Choose Later   ☐ Also copy original message

▷ **Parts:** 1   Plain   **Identity:** Default

Dear Hans,

I had a really cool time at your house and I thought your family was cool too. For a first visit to Germany it was great. Tell your sister I did not mean for that to happen to her Barbie (I guess they <u>are</u> flammable).

The trip to the Black Forest was great! That sticky black resin stuff from the pine tree I climbed has almost come off my pants. Your Mom tried her best (three washes!) but I think my Mom is used to it and she's got it off – mostly. I'm still not allowed to sit on any of the furniture though.

Hey! How's Lotti doing? She is some cat! I'm sure she will be up and about soon enough. Over here we say 'a cat has nine lives'. I guess German cats are different. Of course, I didn't know that when I threw her out of your bedroom window. Neither did I know she was so old, nor about your Dad's cactus just below. So please say to him, 'sorry' – again! Hey, that's the one German word I got used to using and still remember. Trouble is, it's soooo long and the spelling is so weird that I can't write it!

Tell your Grandma 'Hi'. I think we did a pretty good job cleaning her carpet. Those German cookies were so rich and she kept offering me more of that cream stuff, and with all the fizzy pop I'd drunk, well … I hope her carpet is good now. I felt better when I heard her telling your mother it was some old Turkish one your Grandfather had bought her ages ago.

Well, gotta go. Hans, I can't wait for it to be your turn to come to stay with me! I've got loads of fun stuff lined up. You are coming, aren't you?

Your American friend,

Danny

PS. Please answer if you are getting my emails. This is the third one I sent in the last week.

The Exchange Visit

Read the text carefully and circle the best ending for each sentence.

1 It sounds as if Hans' sister's Barbie doll got
   a) lost.
   b) broken.
   c) burnt.

2 Danny's mother
   a) is not bothered about Danny having dirty trousers.
   b) did not clean Danny's trousers as well as Hans' mother did.
   c) knows how to get Danny's trousers clean because he often gets them dirty.

3 When Danny threw the cat out of the window, it
   a) got hurt.
   b) got hurt and damaged the cactus.
   c) damaged the cactus.

4 Hans' grandmother was probably
   a) upset because the old carpet she'd had for years was ruined.
   b) happy because they cleaned the carpet.
   c) not bothered because the carpet was so old.

5 Hans is probably not replying because he
   a) does not want to go and stay with Danny.
   b) is not receiving the emails.
   c) cannot write in English.

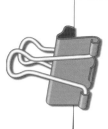

Find out for yourself

Read the email again and underline all the words and phrases that are American English. How would we usually write them? Find out some other words that are completely different in American English.

Dan and Maisie

The afternoon was hot. Between the
balustrades of our veranda, I could see heat shimmering
on the road. A neighbour was scolding a child, telling her not to walk in
the heat and to put her shoes on so that the *bajacs* would not bite her.

Neither Maisie nor I knew what to do with ourselves.
Sweat was collecting behind my knees where they touched
the plastic chair.

'Why don't we go to Miss Jean's and buy some *chenet*, Dan?'

'*Chenet*? Already? It's not the season yet, Maisie.'

'But, Dan, I saw she has some in fresh.'

'Okay. I'm thirsty.'

Careful not to wake Mum, asleep in the hammock under the house,
we slipped from the balcony and walked down to the little shack from
which Miss Jean sold all sorts of things: balls of string, tin buckets,
candles, tin openers and sweets and cold drinks which she kept in a
thermos box with chunks of ice. Around the shack, flowers bloomed and
a hummingbird no bigger than a large bumblebee hovered between their
bright red heads.

'You letting your cousin walk about in this heat, Dan? She's not used
to it,' said Miss Jean from behind the little hatch door of her shack. 'Tell
you Mammy I don't have any *aloo* for her. That husband of mine still hasn't
dug anything up in the garden.'

'It's *chenet* we're after,' we told her.

Later, we sat in the shade of a mango tree on a rock overlooking the
town. We ate the *chenet* and felt its slippery, sweet ripe flesh slide down
our throats. A bird called unseen from the bush, ruffling its feathers.
The sun blazed high in the sky.

Dan and Maisie

Read the text carefully and circle the best ending for each sentence.

1. *Bajacs* must be
   a) dogs.
   b) crawling insects.
   c) flying insects.

2. *Chenet* must be
   a) a fruit.
   b) sweet.
   c) a drink.

3. Maisie must live
   a) nearby.
   b) far away.
   c) in a colder climate.

4. Mum must be Maisie's
   a) aunt.
   b) mother.
   c) grandmother.

5. *Aloo* is most likely to be something
   a) made with sugar.
   b) made with a vegetable.
   c) cold.

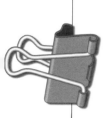

Express yourself

What sort of country do you think this story is set in? Draw one of the scenes as you imagine it. How do you see the characters? What will Miss Jean's shack and the view of the town look like?

What a Genius!

You may have heard of a famous work of art called the *Mona Lisa*. But did you know that the man who painted it also designed the first helicopter, invented the diving bell and knew more about the human body than most doctors at the time?

This remarkable man was Leonardo da Vinci. He lived in Italy in the 1500s and it could be argued that he was the greatest genius the world has ever known. For a man living in the sixteenth century, many of his ideas seem remarkably modern. Drawings for a helicopter design were found in one of his notebooks. Because he lived 500 years ago, Leonardo would not have been able to actually build it, but scientists looking at his plans have said the idea would have worked.

As well as having a highly scientific and inventive mind, Leonardo da Vinci was also a great artist, who combined his interest in colour and shape with an astonishing knowledge of human anatomy. His approach to painting was rather like scientific experimentation. He was always trying new paints and colours. He also planned exactly how he wanted his paintings to look by making dozens of sketches. He filled notebooks with drawings, some of which never made it onto canvas but are a vital record of his creative process.

What a Genius!

Read the text carefully and circle the best ending for each sentence.

1. Many people may not realise that the painter, Leonardo da Vinci
   a) was also called 'Mona Lisa'.
   b) was Italian.
   c) was also a scientist and an inventor.

2. Leonardo da Vinci could not have built a helicopter at the time because
   a) the necessary technology did not exist.
   b) his drawings were not technical enough.
   c) it would have been illegal.

3. Probably the most remarkable thing about Leonardo da Vinci is that
   a) he was such a careful artist.
   b) he painted the *Mona Lisa.*
   c) he knew so much about so many different things.

4. Leonardo da Vinci's notebooks are
   a) full of mistakes.
   b) a record of how he worked.
   c) not as interesting as his finished works of art.

5. Leonardo had a detailed knowledge about the human body
   a) because he was also a doctor.
   b) which made painting more difficult.
   c) which helped him in his painting.

Find out for yourself

Find out where the *Mona Lisa* is hung and why it is thought to be such a great painting.

The average person is said to need 8 hours' sleep a night, although some people seem to function quite happily with 6 or 7 hours or even less. Very young babies are asleep for about 16 hours out of 24. As children grow they sleep less and by the time they are teenagers they usually need about 9 hours.

Sleep experts have found that during the night, we pass through five different stages of sleep. Stages 1 and 2 are light sleep and 3 and 4 are deep sleep. The fifth stage, known as REM sleep, is when we do most of our dreaming. We pass through the whole cycle in approximately an hour and a half, so dreaming occurs several times during the night. Babies spend about half their sleep time in REM sleep, but for an adult it is only about 20 per cent.

No one knows exactly why we need sleep, although it appears to be important for the body to rest and repair itself. Sleep is also thought to play a part in memory and learning. Research has shown that a lack of sleep affects our ability to think and to concentrate. It can also be bad for our general health and make us more prone to illness.

Sleep is something most of us take for granted, but there are some people who have problems with sleeping. Insomnia is the inability to fall or stay asleep, and narcolepsy is a condition which causes people to fall asleep suddenly during the day. Somnambulism is the name given to sleepwalking, a condition which is more common in children than adults.

Sleep

Fill in the gaps, choosing the best word or phrase from the text.

1. On average, the amount of sleep needed by an adult is

   _____ .

2. During the night, we go through a cycle of _____ ,

   then _____ and finally

   _____ .

3. Most people dream _____ times a night.

4. Not getting enough sleep can make a difference to

   _____

   as well as _____ .

5. Problems with sleep include _____ ,

   _____ and _____ .

Find out for yourself

How much sleep do you think you need? What do the initials REM stand for?

Jam in the Park

It's all happening!   Come on down!

Something for all the family

@ Strawberry Fields, Saturday 26 June, 3 p.m. to midnight

Hip-hop/Reggae/Soul/Jungle/Garage bands
with DJ Skooter and DJ Joey 'Toots' McShane

Lookalikes competition (starts 7 p.m.)
Entrants as: Elvis, Leonardo Di Caprio, Britney Spears, Stevie Wonder

There'll be Prizes Prizes Prizes!!

Craft stalls selling hand-made glass, paper, joss sticks, jam, clothes
and much, much more!

Something for the Littlies!

From 4 to 6 p.m.

Bouncy castle (supervised) ~ Tiny tots face painting ~
Pony rides ~ Zongo the Magician

Mystery celebrity guest arriving by helicopter
You've seen her on TV ... Now meet the real she! 9.30 p.m.

Thai, Chinese, Indian, Baked potato, Veggie and Fast-food stands
Eat-all-you-can buffet (£6)   Wine tasting and sales
All-night bar

All proceeds and donations to Help Those In Need,
Registered Charity No. 2X456 HTIN@charitynet.com

Please note: parents or guardians are responsible for their children at all times.
This event sponsored by: Southern Arts, Inc., The Play Shop, Dunn's Beers and Wines, Friends of
Salvador Dali, SaveMarkets Superstore Ltd, Jackson Entertainments, KF-TV, The Bombay Star Restaurant.

Jam in the Park

Fill in the gaps, choosing the best word or phrase from the text.

1. The event is taking place at _____ .

2. If you pay £6, you can have _____ .

3. Entertainments for younger children include

   _____ , _____ ,

   _____ and _____ .

4. Jam in the Park has been organised by _____

   which is a _____ .

5. The Indian food is probably being supplied by

   _____ .

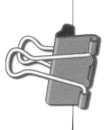

Express yourself

Design a poster for an event to raise money for a charity. It could be a real charity you would like to help or one you have made up.

Sumo Wrestling

Sumo wrestling is the national sport of Japan. It has its origins in the religious ceremonies of Japanese Shinto shrines. There is a lot of ceremony and tradition surrounding this ancient sport and the officials still wear traditional decorated costumes.

In a sumo wrestling contest, the two opponents must each try to throw the other man out of a small ring drawn on the ground. This is not as easy as it may sound; professional sumo wrestlers are huge men with a body weight of at least 130 kg (285 lbs). To build up their weight, sumo wrestlers gorge on a special high-protein, high-fat diet. Weight is vital, as it is harder to throw a heavy opponent out of the ring. Strength is important too, and sumo wrestlers must train so their muscles are strong. Besides weight and strength, a wrestler must also have good technique. Only by keeping his centre of gravity as near to the ground as possible can he resist his opponent's attempts to push him out of the ring. This is the reason sumo wrestlers stand with their legs wide apart, squatting down as low as possible.

It can be quite fascinating to watch two massive men grunting and struggling with each other in the tiny ring. In Japan, fights attract huge crowds and are televised to millions. Championship sumo can last up to 15 days and is held six times a year. Japan's top wrestlers are fabulously rich and adored by their many fans. Yet, apart from some interest in Hawaii, sumo has not caught on in other countries and remains a mainly Japanese sport.

Sumo Wrestling

Fill in the gaps, choosing the best word or phrase from the text.

1. Sumo developed from ceremonies in the _____

   religion.

2. The objective of a sumo wrestling match is to

   _____ .

3. Professional sumo wrestlers eat foods rich in _____

   and _____ .

4. A good sumo wrestler needs to have _____ and

   _____ as well as good

   _____ .

5. There are _____ championship contests a year.

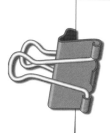

Find out for yourself

Find out about the national sport of another country (not your own).
What are its origins? How do people support it?

Top Ten

Language allows human beings to communicate thoughts and feelings by means of vocal sounds and by the use of written symbols (see Cuneiform, p. 67; Hieroglyphics, p. 68; Pictograms, pp. 69–70; Alphabets, pp. 70–72; Braille, p. 73; Signing, pp. 74–75).

Language	Native speakers (millions)*	Regions where spoken**
1. Mandarin Chinese	800	north and west China
2. English	350	UK, United States, Commonwealth countries
3. Spanish	225	Spain, many countries in Central and South America (not Brazil)
4. Bengali	180	Bangladesh, East India
5. Hindi	180	central India
6. Russian	175	Russia, Ukraine, Kazakhstan, Belarus, Estonia and others
7. Arabic	165	Middle East, North Africa
8. Portuguese	155	Portugal, Brazil
9. Japanese	120	Japan
10. German	120	Austria, Germany, Switzerland

*Figures for 1998   **The language is spoken as a first or official language.*

Top Ten

Fill in the gaps, choosing the best word or phrase from the text.

① Page 68 of this book has information about

_____ .

② Two of the main languages spoken in India are

_____ and _____ .

③ In South American countries, most people speak either

_____ or _____ .

④ The number of people who speak _____

as a first language is over double the number of English speakers.

⑤ This is a list of the ten languages with the greatest number of

_____ , according to the figures in

_____ .

Find out for yourself

Research and compile a 'Top Ten' list for something that interests you.

The United Nations

When the Second World War ended in 1945, an organisation was set up so that such horror could never be repeated. It was known then as the League of Nations and later became the United Nations (UN). The founders of the organisation wrote a treaty, the United Nations Charter, which aimed to prevent future conflict and ensure peace in the world.

Today more than 150 countries are members of the UN. This means that they have signed the UN Charter and agree to obey all the rules.

The UN has its headquarters in a skyscraper on Manhattan Island in New York. This is where representatives of all the countries meet to discuss international affairs. Countries large and small can express their views in the General Assembly and can vote to exclude a country if it has not followed the Charter. Apart from the General Assembly, the UN has several agencies around the world, each dealing with different aspects of international life such as war criminals and children's welfare (UNICEF).

The UN's job of peacekeeping is done in the Security Council. Only five countries (Russia, United States, France, Britain and China) are permanent members of the Security Council. Because these countries were the UN's founders, they have more power. Ten other countries are elected to take part in the work of the Security Council, but only for two years at a time. Some countries think this is unfair.

The United Nations has many critics because it has not always been successful in preventing war. Without the UN, however, there would be nowhere for all countries to meet and discuss important issues, and the world would probably be a more dangerous place.

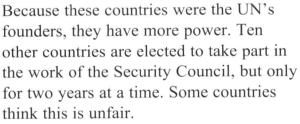
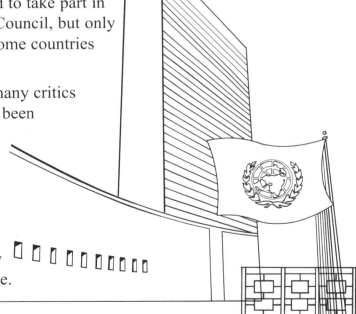

The United Nations

Fill in the gaps, choosing the best word or phrase from the text.

⟨1⟩   The United Nations was founded to avoid further

_____ .

⟨2⟩   The UN has a membership of more than _____

countries.

⟨3⟩   To remain as members of the UN, countries must

_____ of the UN Charter.

⟨4⟩   The UN _____ meets in New York.

⟨5⟩   A total of 15 countries take part in the work of the UN

_____ .

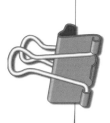

Find out for yourself
Find out more about what the UN does for children.

Table of contents

Zoom 586

Zoom 586

Fill in the gaps, choosing the best word or phrase from the text.

1. If you want to be included in a picture with all your friends, go

   to _____ on page _____.

2. You have finished the film in your camera and you want to take it out,

   so you need _____ on page

   _____ .

3. If the camera strap has come off, you might check

   _____ on page _____ .

4. You are on holiday abroad, the camera has gone wrong and you have

   been unable to fix it yourself. You will need to look at

   _____ for information about

   _____ .

5. You have discovered a small button on the side of the camera and are not

   sure what it is for. You could find out on page _____

   which tells you the _____ .

Find out for yourself

What does the latest camera technology allow you to do?

Jeans

We may think of them as cool, modern and what everybody is wearing. However, jeans first appeared in 1850 and were originally designed as clothing that would be hardwearing and practical rather than fashionable. A gold miner, who was digging for gold in the California gold rush, kept ripping his trousers with the rock samples he put in the pockets. He asked a tailor, Jacob Davis, to make him a tougher pair of trousers. The tailor used a thick cotton fabric which was dyed with a natural blue indigo dye called *bleu de Nimes* (blue from Nimes), after the French town where the dye came from. That is how we got the word 'denim', which is used today for jeans fabric. But, most importantly, Jacob hit on the idea of using copper rivets to strengthen the joins.

The new trousers were such a success with the miners that Jacob Davis decided to patent his idea. He approached Levi Strauss, the wholesaler in New York from whom he bought his cloth. Strauss put up the money for the patent and the two men went into business together.

The original advertisement put out by Levi Strauss and Co. did not contain the word 'jeans'. It announced the arrival of 'spring-bottom pants' and featured the image which can still be seen on the tag of a pair of Levis today: two horses pulling a pair of trousers in different directions. The new overalls soon became popular, not only with miners but with farmers and other workmen too. No one thought of them as fashionable.

It was not until the 1950s that Levi Strauss trousers started to be worn by people other than manual workers. In the 1960s, jeans were featured in the sophisticated fashion magazine *Vogue* and instantly became popular with women. By the 1990s, Calvin Klein was earning $12.5 million a year from producing 'designer' jeans which were proudly worn by movie and pop stars. Presidents, prime ministers and princesses now wear jeans, perhaps to show that they are in touch with ordinary working people. It is probably a good thing that the name 'spring-bottom pants' did not stick – or these trousers might never have become so popular!

Jeans

Fill in the gaps, choosing the best word or phrase from the text.

1 The first jeans were made because a _____

wanted _____ .

2 The word 'denim' comes from the name of a

_____ called _____ .

3 The distinctive new feature in Jacob Davis' trousers was the

_____ .

4 Women only started to wear jeans in _____ .

5 Although jeans were originally worn by _____ ,

they are now worn by all sorts of people including

_____ .

Ask yourself

Do you think we have become obsessed with fashion? Should
advertisements and magazines decide what we wear?

Fill in the gaps, choosing the best word or phrase from the list of possible answers.

Barcelona

This new edition of the *Travelright Guide* to the city of Barcelona has been

①_____ updated by our team of writers and researchers.

Newly expanded and now in full colour, it ②_____ every

aspect of this exciting European city, with its unique culture, colourful history

and daring new architecture.

....

Here is everything you need for an enjoyable and successful visit, including:

★ where to stay – accommodation to suit all budgets from

     ③_____ hotels to youth hostels

★ where to eat – from world-renowned restaurants to best budget meals

★ where to shop – including Barcelona's markets, crafts, fashion stores and

     young ④_____

★ where to find entertainment – clubs and nightlife, excursions out of town

     and all the best beaches of Spain's Costa Brava

All with full details of opening times, prices and transport

Updated annually

'By far the best guide to Barcelona'
The Traveller

'A Travelright Guide is definitely the right choice ... don't leave
⑤_____ without one!'
The Sunday Herald

ISBN 1-85503-384-4

9 781855 033849

Barcelona

①	a) partially	b) badly	c) fully	d) usually
②	a) ignores	b) covers	c) does	d) reads
③	a) luxury	b) cheap	c) over-priced	d) Spanish
④	a) pop stars	b) criminals	c) scientists	d) designers
⑤	a) Spain	b) Barcelona	c) home	d) the bathroom

Express yourself

Describe your ideal holiday. Say what activities you would like to do, what the surroundings and weather would be like and what sort of place you would like to stay in.

Fill in the gaps, choosing the best word or phrase from the list of possible answers.

We see them hanging on poles, blowing in the wind, fluttering on buildings and ships and even

painted on people's faces to support their country's football team.

Flags are an important means of human communication and are used in a variety of ways to give

all sorts of ◇1◇ _____. The study of communication using

signs and symbols is called semiology.

Every country has a flag. It is a symbol for the nation and in some countries it is a criminal

offence to damage or show ◇2◇ _____ to the national flag in any way.

It is taken as an insult to the country itself. In some situations, crowds demonstrating against a

certain country will burn the flag in the streets to show their anger and hatred.

From earliest times, these bright symbols made of cloth have been important in

③ _____ . You had to capture the enemy's flag or standard to win. At the end of the

Second World War, the Russians brought all the Nazi flags they had taken home to Moscow and held a big

ceremony where these awful symbols of Hitler's regime were dumped in a heap.

Flags can be used to mean ④ _____ (a white flag), that an important person has

died (a flag at half-mast), that the winner of a car race has crossed the finish line (a chequered flag) or

that the Queen is in residence at Buckingham Palace.

One flag alone stands on the ⑤ _____ , where no wind blows. It is the

flag of the United States of America. Now, what does that mean?

Flags

① a) messages	b) sentences	c) symbols	d) people
② a) loyalty	b) amusement	c) disrespect	d) your teeth
③ a) peace	b) danger	c) battle	d) cities
④ a) surrender	b) attack	c) victory	d) love
⑤ a) skyscraper	b) North Pole	c) South Pole	d) Moon

Express yourself

Design a flag for your school or family. What colour or symbols will you
use on it?

Fill in the gaps, choosing the best word or phrase from the list of possible answers.

Lifesaver Lizzie Gets Top Award

A **nine-year-old schoolgirl** from West Benton was given a top award after helping to save her dad's

 ① _____ – using

the skills he had taught her.

Lizzie Cardoza was presented with a St John Ambulance First Aider of the Year award at a glittering ceremony on Friday.

② _____

Lizzie was on hand to help her diabetic father after he fell unconscious at the wheel of their car. Her dad had suffered a hypoglycaemic attack as a result of low blood sugar. Lizzie, who is a St John Ambulance cadet, kept her cool

③ _____ first aid tips she had learned from her father, a division officer of the local group.

When her father became ill in Bateson Road, Lizzie turned off the engine and took the key from the car. She then asked a woman driver to call an ambulance on her mobile. She tried to give her dad some chocolate, but he couldn't be woken. 'I was getting a bit <4> _____,' said Lizzie, 'But when I saw the ambulance arrive, I knew everything would be OK.' Paramedics were quick to arrive on the scene and give treatment.

Mr Cardoza, 49, made a full <5> _____. He later said, 'She's done really well. I think many adults wouldn't have coped as well as she did. People who were there said she was very grown up.'

Lifesaver Lizzie Gets Top Award

<1> a) time b) money c) life d) energy

<2> a) Quick-thinking b) Lively c) Lovely d) Fast-talking

<3> a) except for b) thanks to c) in spite of d) as well as

<4> a) hungry b) bored c) cross d) worried

<5> a) statement b) recovery c) confession d) apology

Express yourself

Get a copy of a local newspaper and look for a news report that interests you. Rewrite it, giving only the really important facts. Your report should be half as long as the original. Give it a new headline.

Fill in the gaps, choosing the best word or phrase from the list of possible answers.

Gorillas

After humans, some of the most intelligent creatures on this planet

are the apes. This group ⟨1⟩ _____ chimpanzees,

orang-utans and gorillas. Closely related to human beings, apes have

large brains; long arms, fingers and toes; and body hair. In fact, human

beings are sometimes given the nickname ⟨2⟩ '_____ ape'

because human body hair is not as thick and long as that of apes.

People have always been fascinated by apes, and perhaps by none

more than the gorilla. They are very large – a male 'silverback' gorilla

can measure just over 2 metres (6 feet) and weigh 180 kg (400 lb).

They can look very fierce, and films such as *King Kong* have given this

species a reputation of being very ⟨3⟩ _____ . In

fact, nothing could be further from the truth; gorillas are very

peaceful animals and only become violent if provoked.

Gorillas are normally slow, gentle creatures who spend their time in

family groups, grooming each other and feeding on leaves and shoots

in the forest. Yes, gorillas are vegetarians! Some researchers have followed and studied gorilla families as they move around the forest. The researchers

found that the gorillas, although they were ④ _____ at first,

gradually came to accept them. In some cases, the gorillas became trusting enough to

⑤ _____ the researchers, looking for lice to pick out of their hair!

Their experience of these apes completely

dispels the myth of gorillas

as chest-thumping hostile

predators, as shown in

some films.

Gorillas

① a) includes   b) excludes   c) selects   d) numbers

② a) intelligent   b) naked   c) hairy   d) city

③ a) lovable   b) envious   c) aggressive   d) artistic

④ a) nasty   b) hungry   c) sleepy   d) cautious

⑤ a) attack   b) groom   c) feed   d) ignore

Find out for yourself

Find out about one of the other species of ape.

Fill in the gaps, choosing the best word or phrase from the list of possible answers.

It Started Well

It was Saturday morning and the sun was streaming in through the open window. I opened my eyes to see the curtain billowing in the wind. I felt completely ①_____ . The birds were chanting their morning songs, calling to their mates and singing to the world. I glanced over at my clock: 8.55. I got up and walked across the landing to the bathroom. I splashed my face with cool refreshing water.

The water fell off my body gracefully. I watched it swirl down the drain, going down into nothingness. I soaped quickly as I heard my mum shout something up the stairs. 'Ebony, get a move on! We have to get there early.'

It was the day of my school's summer fair. My mum, my brother and I were running a cookies and lemonade stall and generally helping out. Mum and Mrs Sandpiper were the main ②_____ of the fair. Mum is always helping out at my school. It's kind of ③_____ , if you ask me. Well, what 11-year-old wants their mum helping out at school?

But still, it'd be good fun. Cassie and I would do our

④ _____ on the stall and then we would be able to go round the fair. There's always loads of cake and stuff to buy and last year Mr Willis ran a 'Soak the teacher' game. Of course, we were hoping to get a shot at Ms Simpson!

As I ran down the stairs, I smelt ⑤ _____ . The kitchen was filled with black clouds and the smoke alarm was beeping …

It Started Well

①   a) exhausted   b) calm   c) terrified   d) alone

②   a) organisers   b) sponsors   c) attractions   d) helpers

③   a) cool   b) interesting   c) boring   d) embarrassing

④   a) dance   b) shift   c) cooking   d) homework

⑤   a) cooking   b) bacon   c) burning   d) toast

Express yourself

Write your own version of how you think this story might continue.

Fill in the gaps, choosing the best word or phrase from the list of possible answers.

Holiday Diary

August 4

We've arrived. Have come up to bedroom alone. A spooky-looking house, but a huge garden with lots of trees and a pond. Two weeks without my friends! How will I survive?

Have to share with Timmy – ugh! He'll probably have
① _____ and wet the bed. Loads of bedrooms, but Mum says he'll be scared on his own. Baby! Keep hearing odd noises in the attic. Mice?

August 6

Last night, a storm. Thunder rumbling and lightning ② _____. Dad had to go around closing the shutters. Roof ancient. Mum put buckets and basins on floor to catch leaks. Thunder terrifying. Attic noises worse than ever – like someone ③ _____ and trying to get out. Dad says don't be silly and don't frighten Timmy.

August 9

Sure there's something in attic. Too loud for mice. Like knocking. Like someone trapped. Got into Timmy's bed (so he wouldn't be too scared).

August 11

Woke in middle of night. Raining outside. Strange noise from attic again. Got into Timmy's bed. He wasn't there! I was all alone! Ran to Mum and Dad's room. Timmy in with them. We all got in together (said I was cold).

August 13

Told Timmy if he sleeps in our room I'll buy him a chocolate bar. Says he'll think about it. So tired. I've got dark circles round my eyes. Want to tell Mum and Dad but they'll only call me silly. Can't wait to go home.

August 14

Timmy stayed. I had to promise him three (!) chocolate bars and a bag of crisps. Little brothers! I hope they make him ④ _____ . AND had to promise he can use my Walkman. Or he'll tell Dad I'm a scaredy-cat. Got to be nice to Timmy. But wait till we get home ...

August 15

Very windy again. Sitting by pond this afternoon, looking at house. Trees ⑤ _____ all around it. Suddenly realised. That was the noise – my ghost trapped in the attic! It was the branch of a tree!

As I told Timmy, easy mistake to make.

Holiday Diary

① a) nightmares   b) problems   c) biscuits   d) fever

② a) dazzling   b) flashing   c) shining   d) glaring

③ a) singing   b) banging   c) dancing   d) talking

④ a) happy   b) glad   c) behave   d) sick

⑤ a) swaying   b) growing   c) dying   d) blossoming

Ask yourself

Are you afraid of something, or do you know someone who is? What is it? What can you do about it?

Fill in the gaps, choosing the best word or phrase from the list of possible answers.

Ants

Ants may seem tiny and insignificant, but there are a lot of them on this planet. In fact, ants far

①_____

humans and there are 14,000 different species. Like humans, ants are social creatures. They live in highly organised and sophisticated groups called colonies, in which each ant has a specialised ②_____ .

Soldier ants, for example, have large jaws, which makes them ideal for guarding the anthill entrances, just like sentries. The queen is the only female in the anthill to breed. She mates with one of the males and spends the rest of her life laying eggs to ③_____ the colony.

All the other females are worker ants. Their main task is to forage for food outside the anthill. This they regurgitate to feed the rest of the colony. This means that all the other ants live on food already chewed and partly ④_____ by the workers. The workers also look after the eggs and larvae and are responsible for cleaning the anthill.

Ants have a highly developed system for obtaining large quantities of nutritious plant juices. Just as we farm cows, putting them out to pasture and then ⟨5⟩ _____ them, ants farm small green insects called aphids. These are kept in corrals deep inside the anthill and then taken out by shepherd ants to feed on the juices of plant stems. When they are full, the shepherds herd them back into the anthill and 'milk' them. The ants tickle the stomachs of the aphids so that they release the juices. These juices are stored or fed to larvae in the ant nursery.

Ants

⟨1⟩ a) overtake b) outnumber c) defeat d) outrun

⟨2⟩ a) role b) head c) department d) cell

⟨3⟩ a) feed b) overtake c) populate d) defend

⟨4⟩ a) cooked b) tasted c) swallowed d) digested

⟨5⟩ a) grazing b) milking c) feeding d) riding

Ask yourself

Ants and humans are both social animals. How is the way ants live similar to the way we live and how is it different?

Answers

Getting the main idea

The Fighting Spiders of Japan

1) a. 2) b. 3) b. 4) c. 5) a.

Scribble

1) b. 2) a. 3) b. 4) c. 5) c.

Out and About

1) c. 2) b. 3) a. 4) b. 5) b.

Life Support

1) b. 2) a. 3) c. 4) b. 5) a.

Windy Willows

1) c. 2) b. 3) a. 4) c. 5) c.

Professor Stephen Hawking

1) b. 2) a. 3) c. 4) c. 5) b.

Andes Adventure

1) b. 2) c. 3) a. 4) b. 5) c.

To Autumn

1) b. 2) c. 3) a. 4) c. 5) b.

Making inferences

Trepanning

1) b. 2) a. 3) a. 4) b. 5) c.

Letters to the Editor

1) b. 2) a. 3) c. 4) b. 5) a.

The Labyrinth

1) a. 2) b. 3) b. 4) c. 5) a.

The Round Table

1) b. 2) a. 3) c. 4) a. 5) b.

The Exchange Visit

1) c. 2) c. 3) b. 4) a. 5) a.

Dan and Maisie

1) b. 2) a. 3) c. 4) a. 5) b.

What a Genius!

1) c. 2) a. 3) c. 4) b. 5) c.

Noting details

Sleep

1) 8 hours 2) light sleep, deep sleep, REM sleep
3) several 4) our ability to think and to concentrate, our general health
5) insomnia, narcolepsy, somnambulism

Jam in the Park

1) Strawberry Fields
2) Eat-all-you-can buffet
3) bouncy castle, face painting, pony rides, Zongo the Magician.
4) Help Those In Need, registered charity
5) The Bombay Star Restaurant

Sumo Wrestling

1) Shinto 2) throw the other man out of a small ring 3) protein, fat
4) weight, strength, technique 5) six

Top Ten

1) hieroglyphics
2) Hindi, Bengali
3) Spanish. Portuguese
4) Mandarin Chinese
5) native speakers, 1998

The United Nations

1) war/conflict 2) 150

3) follow all the rules
4) General Assembly
5) Security Council

Zoom 586

1) Self-timer photography, page 29 2) Unloading film, page 22 3) Strap attachment, page 7
4) the back cover, Zoom dealers (international)
5) 1, names of working parts

Jeans

1) gold miner, a tougher pair of trousers 2) dye, bleu de Nimes 3) copper rivets 4) the 1960s
5) manual workers, presidents, prime ministers and princesses.

Using context clues

Barcelona

1) c. 2) b. 3) a. 4) d. 5) c.

Flags

1) a. 2) c. 3) c. 4) a. 5) d.

Lifesaver Lizzie Gets Top Award

1) c. 2) a. 3) b. 4) d. 5) b.

Gorillas

1) a. 2) b. 3) c. 4) d. 5) b.

It Started Well

1) b. 2) a. 3) d. 4) b. 5) c.

Holiday Diary

1) a. 2) b. 3) b. 4) d. 5) a.

Ants

1) b. 2) a. 3) c. 4) d. 5) b.